My Big Book
of Fairies
belongs to:

...Aoife..................

ORCHARD BOOKS
338 Euston Road, London NW1 3BH
Orchard Books Australia
Level 17/207 Kent Street, Sydney, NSW 2000

First published in 2014 by Orchard Books

A CIP catalogue record for this book is available from the British Library.

ISBN 978 1 40833 543 7
1 3 5 7 9 10 8 6 4 2

Printed in China

The paper and board used in this paperback are natural recyclable products made from wood grown in sustainable forests.
The manufacturing processes conform to the environmental regulations of the country of origin.

Orchard Books is a division of Hachette Children's Books, an Hachette UK company

www.hachette.co.uk

RAINBOW magic™

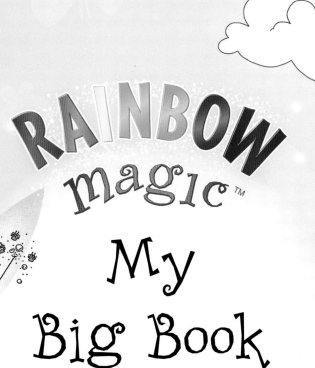

My Big Book of Fairies

Contents

Dear Fairy Friend,

Welcome to this very special book! It's wonderful to see you all. In just a few magical moments you'll meet all the fairies from Fairyland – some old friends and some new – and you'll learn lots of fascinating things about every single one!

We would like to thank you for being such wonderful, loyal friends of the Rainbow Magic Fairies. Dearest Kirsty and Rachel have shown us that human children are the kindest creatures in the whole world! Your belief in magic and fairies makes us feel very happy and proud, and we can't wait to have lots more amazing adventures with you.

With love
and thanks,

King Oberon
and
Queen Titania

Hello dear friend,
Come take a peek,
So many fairies for you to meet!
There's Ruby, Bella, Tia too,
Lots and lots of friends for you.
You'll learn so much
About them all,
Magic and fun –
We'll have a ball!

Ruby
the Red Fairy

Ruby's the fairy that everyone knows. With roses in her hair and on the tips of her toes!

Ruby is very special to Rachel and Kirsty as she's the very first fairy they ever met! Ruby and her six rainbow sisters were banished from Fairyland by mean Jack Frost's spell. Rachel and Kirsty found Ruby by following a beautiful rainbow across Rainspell Island.

Rainbow Reveal
Ruby's dress is made from hundreds of tiny rose petals!

Did you know?

Some cultures believe that the colour red brings luck and joy!

Rainbow Reveal
Ruby's favourite foods are super-sweet strawberries and jam tarts.

Rainbow Fairies

Amber
the Orange Fairy

Rachel and Kirsty found Amber trapped in a seashell on the beach! They freed her with the help of a magical golden feather.

Rainbow Reveal
When Amber uses her wand it releases shimmering bubbles that smell of zingy oranges!

Rainbow Reveal
Sparkly yellow butterflies emerge from Saffron's wand each time she waves it.

Jack Frost's spell sent Saffron tumbling into a beehive! Luckily this friendly fairy had a lovely time with the bees and even made a very special bee friend called Queenie.

Saffron
the Yellow Fairy

Fern
the Green Fairy

Rainbow Reveal
Fern's best friend is a grey squirrel called Fluffy!

Rainbow Reveal
There are 13 fairies who dress in different shades of green.

Fern's adventure took place in a secret garden! Rachel and Kirsty had to make their way through a maze to find Fern, watching out for some very naughty goblins. With the help of some friendly animals and a magical fairy firework, Fern was finally reunited with her rainbow sisters!

Did you know?
The colour green is said to represent growth and harmony!

Rainbow Reveal
Santa Claus originally wore a green suit!

Rainbow Fairies

Sky
the Blue Fairy

Rachel and Kirsty had to scare off some ice-skating goblins to rescue Sky from a frozen rockpool. Sky was so cold her rainbow sisters needed to form a fairy ring to bring back her magical sparkles.

Rainbow Reveal
Whenever Sky waves her wand a shower of sparkling blue stars appears.

Izzy
the Indigo Fairy

Izzy's adventure took place in the enchanted Land of Sweets! In this story the girls and Izzy met the Sugarplum Fairy and rode in a pink bubblegum balloon.

Rainbow Reveal
Izzy's magic turns everything she touches a beautiful indigo colour!

Heather
the Violet Fairy

Did you know?

Rainbows appear
when raindrops
reflect sunlight.

Rachel and Kirsty had to reunite Heather with her rainbow sisters before their holiday on Rainspell Island came to an end! Luckily, a magical ride on a merry-go-round led them to the little fairy. But then the fairies had to face cruel Jack Frost and his gang of goblins…

Rainbow Reveal

A rainbow is a beautiful multicoloured arc of light in the sky.

Rainbow Reveal

Heather's magic allows her to create fizzing lilac bubbles. These can grow large enough to trap Jack Frost!

Rainbow Fairies

11

Crystal
the Snow Fairy

With one quick wave of a magical feather, These seven fairies can control the weather!

Because Jack Frost and his goblins had stolen the Weather Fairies' feathers, the weather in Fairyland and the human world turned totally topsy-turvy! Rachel and Kirsty had to help Crystal find her magical Snow Feather and return it to Doodle the weather-vane cockerel.

Did you know?
The world's biggest snowman was built in Maine, USA, in 2008, and stood at over 37 metres tall!

Rainbow Reveal
At the start of Crystal's story, Queen Titania gives Rachel and Kirsty two lockets filled with magical fairy dust.

Rainbow Reveal
The girls use this fairy dust in lots of their Rainbow Magic adventures!

In the hands of a very naughty goblin, Abigail's breeze feather once caused chaos at the Wetherbury Village Fete. With the help of a plucky puppy called Twiglet, the girls and Abigail found the magical feather, high in the sky!

Abigail
the Breeze Fairy

Rainbow Reveal
Breezy autumn is Abigail's favourite time of year – she loves to fly among the falling golden leaves!

Pearl
the Cloud Fairy

The magic of the cloud feather made everyone very grumpy when it was taken from its rightful fairy owner, Pearl!

Rainbow Reveal
Non-magical clouds are made up of very tiny droplets of water or ice crystals.

Weather Fairies

Goldie
the Sunshine Fairy

Rainbow Reveal
Goldie really is a little ray of sunshine! She's super-smiley, warm-hearted and full of giggles.

Did you know?
The sun is actually a star! It's the closest star to Earth, and is nearly 5 billion years old.

Did you know?
The city of Yuma in the USA is the sunniest place on Earth. There, the sun shines 94% of the time!

Everyone loves the sunshine! But when Goldie's magic sunshine feather was stolen from Doodle the weather-vane cockerel, the sun shone so much that it was far too hot in Wetherbury.

Evie's mist feather creates sparkly wisps of mist that make things look very pretty! But in the hands of a naughty goblin, the feather can cause all sorts of misty mischief.

Evie
the Mist Fairy

Rainbow Reveal
Goblins are scared of mist as they think Pogwurzels will be able to sneak up behind them!

Storm
the Lightning Fairy

Rainbow Reveal
Lightning is a bright flash of electricity produced by a thunderstorm.

Rachel and Kirsty had a very dramatic adventure with Storm the Lightning Fairy! They came face to face with a mean goblin and Storm's powerful lightning feather, inside a dusty old museum.

Weather Fairies

Hayley
the Rain Fairy

Because horrid Jack Frost had stolen her magical rain feather, in Hayley's adventure the rain just wouldn't stop falling! With Hayley's help, the girls paddled through a flood to return all seven magical weather feathers to Doodle.

Did you know?

The rainiest place in the world is Cherrapunji, India. It can rain up to 500 inches per year.

Did you know?

Rain is recycled water that evaporated from the world's lakes, rivers and oceans!

Cherry
the Cake Fairy

Cherry the Cake Fairy
loves to bake
The most delicious
party cakes!

Queen Titania and King Oberon's 1,000th jubilee was a very happy occasion, and the Party Fairies were on hand to make the celebrations extra special! But mean Jack Frost was determined to spoil the fun. Rachel and Kirsty had to help Cherry find her missing party bag so she could bake a magical cake fit for the royal couple!

Did you know?

Cherry's frilly red
skirt looks just like
an upside-down fairy
cake case!

Rainbow Reveal

Cherry loves all
cakes but her very
favourite is a cherry
jam tart. Yummy!

Party Fairies

17

Melodie
the Music Fairy

Poor Kirsty's ballet show was almost ruined when a naughty goblin stole Melodie's party bag and caused musical mayhem!

Rainbow Reveal
Goblins love music. But the silly creatures are actually tone-deaf and have no sense of rhythm!

Grace
the Glitter Fairy

When Grace's magical bag went missing, all glittery party decorations lost their sparkle.

Rainbow Reveal
Grace's favourite party foods are Cherry's fairy cakes – covered in edible glitter!

Honey
the Sweet Fairy

No party is complete without some delicious sweet treats. Honey's adventure took place in Mrs Twist's Sweet Shop, which is full of all the sweets you could ever dream of! But when a goblin tried to snatch Honey's party bag, the shop got into a very sticky situation.

Rainbow Reveal

Honey and her fairy helpers love inventing new sweets. They have lots of fun trying out their creations on the other Party Fairies!

Party Fairies

Polly
the Party Fun Fairy

Polly the Party Fun Fairy makes sure that every party has brilliant games for everyone to enjoy! So it was very important that the girls helped Polly to find her party bag when it went missing.

Rainbow Reveal
When Polly uses the fairy dust in her party bag, beautiful blue balloons appear!

Phoebe
the Fashion Fairy

Phoebe makes sure that everyone looks fairy fabulous at parties and celebrations, with fashionable frocks and amazing accessories!

Rainbow Reveal
The silk used to make Phoebe's dress is from magical silkworms. The dress glimmers and shimmers in every light!

Jasmine
the Present Fairy

People have been giving each other presents for many hundreds of years. It is likely the tradition goes back to Roman times.

Jasmine's magic makes presents and prizes perfect for everyone! This special magical power has to be looked after very carefully. So when they met Jasmine, Rachel and Kirsty had to protect her bag and get to the King and Queen's 1,000th jubilee party on time.

Rainbow Reveal
At the end of the Party Fairies' stories, Rachel and Kirsty are each given a musical jewellery box by the fairy king and queen.

Rainbow Reveal
Jasmine is named after a delicate, beautifully scented flower.

Party Fairies

India
the Moonstone Fairy

Rainbow Reveal
It is believed that moonstones bring good luck.

The Jewel Fairies each have a precious stone. India's beautiful moonstone helps to make sure that everyone has sweet dreams. When Jack Frost stole the seven magical jewels, Rachel and Kirsty had to help the Jewel Fairies return them to Queen Titania's tiara – or all fairy magic would have faded away!

Nasty Jack Frost stole each fairy's jewel, And used them for magical deeds foul and cruel!

Did you know?

The glowing shimmer that surrounds the moonstone is said to resemble moonlight.

Rainbow Reveal
When all of the Jewel Fairies' jewels are in Queen Titania's tiara, a magical rainbow is formed once a year. The fairies use this to recharge their magic!

Scarlett's jewel has the power to make things bigger and smaller, so in her story it was very important that her garnet was returned. Otherwise Kirsty and Rachel might have stayed tiny forever!

Scarlett
the Garnet Fairy

Rainbow Reveal
Scarlett and Ruby once held a party where everyone had to dress in red!

Emily
the Emerald Fairy

Rainbow Reveal
If you were born in May, then the deep-green emerald is your birthstone!

Emily's adventure took place in a wonderful toy shop! But with the missing jewel affecting Emily's special ability to see into the future, things were not always what they seemed…

Jewel Fairies

Chloe
the Topaz Fairy

Chloe's golden topaz went missing at Halloween, one of the most mystical times of year... With Chloe's magical jewel missing, her ability to change one thing into something else caused all kinds of tricks and treats at a fancy-dress shop in Tippington.

Did you know?
The Queen of England's Crown Jewels contain 23,578 precious stones.

Did you know?
The word Topaz is derived from Topazos, a small island in the Red Sea, where the Romans first discovered the stone.

Rainbow Reveal
Chloe's jewel is a beautiful golden colour, but topaz can actually come in many different colours!

Amy
the Amethyst Fairy

Amy's magical amethyst controls appearing and disappearing magic – she can make things invisible! When Amy's jewel went missing, the girls had a very odd adventure, high up in a treehouse!

Rainbow Reveal
Amy sometimes uses her magic to help Polly the Party Fun Fairy with her party games!

Sophie
the Sapphire Fairy

Rainbow Reveal
Sophie is a great friend of Zara the Starlight Fairy. The sapphires that flow from Sophie's wand look so beautiful in Zara's starlight!

Sophie's sparkling sapphire looks after wishing magic! With her jewel lost in the human world, wishes everywhere were in a terrible muddle…

Jewel Fairies

Lucy
the Diamond Fairy

In the final Jewel Fairies adventure, Rachel and Kirsty travelled to Fairyland to help Lucy find her diamond, which controls flying magic. The girls had to avoid scary Jack Frost's ice bolts so they could return the diamond to Queen Titania's tiara!

Did you know?

This precious jewel can be found in a variety of colours, even black!

Rainbow Reveal

Kirsty and Rachel see a huge, glittering diamond just before they meet Elizabeth the Jubilee Fairy. This diamond is called the Great Star of Africa.

Rainbow Reveal

The girls love flying but Kirsty sometimes finds it a bit scary, especially when she's a fairy and Jack Frost is chasing her!

Katie
the Kitten Fairy

Katie's the fairy with a cute magic kitten,
One purr from Shimmer, and you will be smitten!

The Pet Keeper Fairies make sure that all pets in Fairyland and the human world have happy homes. But when the seven magical pets were kidnapped, the fairies' magic stopped working! Rachel and Kirsty love animals and were happy to try and reunite the fairies with their beloved pets in the seven Pet Keeper Fairies adventures.

Did you know?
All kittens are born with blue eyes. They don't develop their true eye colour until they are about three months old!

Rainbow Reveal
Kirsty has a gorgeous kitten called Pearl.

Rainbow Reveal
There are three fairies who have cute pet cats!

Pet Keeper Fairies

27

Bella
the Bunny Fairy

Rainbow Reveal
Misty lives in a cosy burrow underneath Bella's pretty toadstool house.

If ever a bunny is in trouble, it's Bella to the rescue! Her enchanted helper is a fluffy rabbit called Misty who twitches her nose and is always changing colour.

Georgia
the Guinea Pig Fairy

Georgia's adventure took place on Strawberry Farm. Rachel and Kirsty had to deal with some very odd sheep to reunite Georgia and her super-cute guinea pig, Sparky!

Rainbow Reveal
Guinea pigs are very sociable animals. Sparky loves to play with all the other magic pets!

Rainbow Reveal
Wild guinea pigs live in South America!

Lauren
the Puppy Fairy

The girls were having a wonderful time at the Wetherbury Spring Fair when they met Sunny, Lauren's magic puppy. But it was a race against time to reunite him with Lauren before some bouncing goblins could snatch him!

Rainbow Reveal
Rachel has a dog called Buttons!

Rainbow Reveal
In Fairyland, pets choose their owners – not like in the human world where it's the other way round!

Did you know?
The biggest number of puppies ever born in a litter was 24!

Pet Keeper Fairies

Harriet
the Hamster Fairy

Rainbow Reveal
Hamsters have pouches in their cheeks, where they store food.

There naughty goblins set a tricky trap for Twinkle the magic hamster in Harriet's adventure. Kirsty and Rachel had to reach him before the goblins could!

Molly
the Goldfish Fairy

There were some very cunning goblins disguised as gnomes in Molly's story. And they stole Flash, Molly's magic goldfish! Luckily, Flash was very clever and managed to swim back to Molly.

Rainbow Reveal
The oldest goldfish ever lived to be 43 years old! His name was Tish.

R achel and Kirsty were having a lovely pony ride in the forest when Glitter the magic pony arrived in a twinkle of fairy magic! Unfortunately a gang of seven goblins threatened to spook all the ponies with their mischievous ways. And then Jack Frost arrived…

Penny
the Pony Fairy

Did you know?

There are over 300 different breeds of horse in the world. A pony is a small horse measuring under 14.2 hands high.

Rainbow Reveal

In this set of adventures, Jack Frost was determined to steal all of the Pet Keeper Fairies' special animal friends. Although this was very naughty, it turned out that Jack really wanted a magical pet of his own!

Rainbow Reveal

Both Rachel and Kirsty love horseriding. They have more horsey fun with Helena the Horseriding Fairy!

Pet Keeper Fairies

Megan
the Monday Fairy

Megan and her sisters each have a magic flag, But when the flags go missing, every day's a drag!

Did you know?

The word Monday comes from an ancient Anglo-Saxon word meaning 'the moon's day'.

When the girls met Megan, it turned out that Jack Frost had been up to his old tricks again! With their seven magical flags missing, the Fun Day Fairies couldn't make any day *anywhere* enjoyable. They had to find their flags and charge their wands – or lose their magical powers for ever and ever…

Rainbow Reveal
Every morning, Francis the Royal Time Guard looks in the Fairyland Book of Days to check which day it is.

Tallulah
the Tuesday Fairy

With Tallulah's magical flag missing, this pretty fairy couldn't help anyone have a good time on a Tuesday! That meant that Rachel's sports day was no fun at all.

Willow
the Wednesday Fairy

In this adventure, Rachel and Kirsty had to find Willow's flag at the Tippington Arts and Crafts Fair. The trouble was that it was the perfect place for naughty goblins to hide!

Fun Day Fairies

Thea
the Thursday Fairy

Did you know?

Every year in America, Thanksgiving Day takes place on the fourth Thursday of November.

Thea's story took place in an aquarium! It was a magical place for the girls to visit – there were sea horses, crabs, sharks, otters and a reef to see… Oh, and some troublesome goblins were there too, and they wanted Thea's fun day flag!

Rainbow Reveal
Kirsty and Rachel love to speed through the water with their fairy friends! Fairy magic makes them warm and dry as soon as they're back on land.

Rainbow Reveal
Thea's favourite thing to do on a Thursday morning is to teach young fairies how to dance a fairy jig!

Freya
the Friday Fairy

Rainbow Reveal

Freya is very arty and teaches the other Fun Day Fairies how to paint pretty pictures.

Everyone loves Fridays – but when Freya's beautiful lilac flag went missing, no one in either the fairy or human worlds had that fun Friday feeling!

Sienna
the Saturday Fairy

Rainbow Reveal

All of the Fun Day Fairies' flags have a picture of the sun on them. Everyone feels full of sunshine and happiness when the flags are working their magic!

Even a fabulous fashion show couldn't make the Saturday in Sienna's story fun! Luckily, her flag was somewhere backstage at the show – but so were a gang of thieving goblins…

Fun Day Fairies

Sarah
the Sunday Fairy

Did you know?

Sunday is known as both the first, and the last, day of the week! It just depends on what religion you follow.

Sunday is traditionally known as a day of rest, but there was no rest for Rachel and Kirsty in this final Fun Day adventure. A picnic at Windy Lake was the girls' last chance to reunite Sarah with her magic flag. But first they had to persuade a frosty visitor to help them!

Rainbow Reveal
Phoebe the Fashion Fairy uses her magic to change the colours of Sarah's stripy tights for special occasions!

Rainbow Reveal
At the end of the Fun Day adventures, Queen Titania gave Rachel and Kirsty a glittering kite each! Each time they fly their kites, the girls think of their fairy friends.

Tia
the Tulip Fairy

The Petal Fairies make sure that flowers everywhere grow beautifully, bringing lots of happiness and joy to everyone! But when Jack Frost stole the petals and scattered them around the human world, Rachel and Kirsty had a tough job to return Tia's tulip petal to her…

When the magic petals are taken away, No flowers can bloom to brighten each day…

Did you know?

Tulips come in a huge variety of colours, including red, purple and orange.

Rainbow Reveal

Jack Frost secretly wishes he had green fingers. He wants pretty flowers to grow in his icy garden!

Petal Fairies

Pippa
the Poppy Fairy

Pippa's adventure took place in a pretty flower shop, but with the magic petals missing, all the flowers were droopy! The girls had to outwit a whole gang of naughty goblins to find Pippa's poppy petal and return it to Fairyland.

Rainbow Reveal
Bright red poppies are worn by many people each November to remember those who have fought in wars.

Louise
the Lily Fairy

In this story, Rachel and Kirsty row a boat on a lovely lake full of lily pads! But with Louise's magic petal in the hands of the pesky goblins, the lily pads had no flowers…

Rainbow Reveal
In Chinese culture the lily means 'forever in love'!

Charlotte
the Sunflower Fairy

Charlotte's cheery sunflower is a firm fairy favourite. When Jack Frost took her magic petal, everyone was very unhappy to see her stunning flowers wilting. So it was very important that Rachel and Kirsty helped this pretty little fairy get her petal back so her flowers could stand tall in the sunshine once more!

Did you know?

The tallest sunflower ever grown was over eight metres high. That's more than twice as tall as the average house!

Did you know?

Sunflowers are very easy to grow! Plant each seed in a sunny and sheltered place in the garden. Water well and in about two weeks you'll see sunflower shoots coming up. Magical!

Petal Fairies

Olivia
the Orchid Fairy

Rainbow Reveal
Each magic petal protects a certain type of flower, but all the petals look after every other flower and plant in the world, too!

The orchid is a very delicate flower. When they met Olivia, Rachel and Kirsty had to help her get her pretty blue and purple petal back from the goblins before the clumsy creatures destroyed it.

Danielle
the Daisy Fairy

In her adventure, Danielle and the girls had to dodge a storm of icy hailstones to get her magic petal back from the mean goblins! Luckily, the fairy friends had some help from a very long, magical daisy chain!

Rainbow Reveal
The name 'Daisy' comes from the Old English word meaning 'day's eye' – because daisies open at dawn!

Ella
the Rose Fairy

A flower show set in some beautiful gardens was where Kirsty and Rachel had their adventure with Ella the Rose Fairy! In this final Petal Fairies story, the girls had to flutter through Chaney Court Hedge Maze, and come face to face with chaos-causing goblins, to find Ella's beautiful petal.

Did you know?

There are over 100 different species of rose!

Did you know?

Roses of different colours represent different emotions. A yellow rose means friendship, a pink rose symbolises happiness and a red rose shows love and respect!

Rainbow Reveal

When it's the other Petal Fairies' birthdays, Ella sews together fallen rose petals to make pretty gifts.

Petal Fairies

Bethany
the Ballet Fairy

The Dance Fairies love
to sway and to move,
But without their ribbons,
the world's lost its groove!

All seven Dance Fairies were cast into the human world by dastardly Jack Frost, and he took their magic ribbons! Nobody could enjoy dancing in the human world or in Fairyland until Rachel and Kirsty helped the fairies get their ribbons back.

Rainbow Reveal

Bethany is a wonderful ballet dancer, and always wears her leotard, tutu and ballet shoes! She has over twenty pairs of soft ballet pumps, in lots of different beautiful colours.

Rainbow Reveal

In this story, Kirsty and Rachel are going to see *Swan Lake*, a very famous ballet about a swan princess.

Rainbow Reveal

Bethany teaches the little Rainbow Magic fairies how to dance. They look very sweet practising their pliés in tiny fairy tutus!

Jade
the Disco Fairy

Jade is a real disco star in her swirly green hipsters and funky top! In her story, it was the day of Kirsty's school disco. But although Jade looks ready to hit the dance floor, with her magical ribbon missing, nobody was in the party mood...

Rainbow Reveal
Silly Jack Frost stole the Dance Fairies' ribbons because he wanted his goblin servants to dance well at his party!

Rebecca
the Rock 'n' Roll Fairy

Kirsty's parents were going to a rock 'n' roll dance in this adventure, but the girls knew that if Rebecca's ribbon wasn't returned to her quickly, the dance would be a disaster...

Rainbow Reveal
Rock 'n' roll dancing is very energetic, with lots of jumps, throws and lifts.

Dance Fairies

Tasha
the Tap Dance Fairy

Rainbow Reveal
Tasha loves to perform in front of her fairy friends. Sometimes she teams up with Leah the Theatre Fairy, and together they put on a great show!

Rachel and Kirsty were at an open day at Wetherbury College in this adventure when a gang of toe-tapping goblins attracted their attention! The girls and Tasha had to work out a cunning plan to distract the goblins so they could return the magic ribbon to its rightful owner.

Did you know?
The 'tap' of tap dance comes from metal sections that are fitted into the toes and heels of the special shoes. This makes them tap on the floor!

Did you know?
Due to the 'tapping' noise that special tap shoes make on the floor, tap dance is sometimes thought of as a form of music!

The girls were invited to a grown-up party in this story, with a cool jazz band. But Rachel and Kirsty knew that because Jessica's magic ribbon was missing, disaster would soon strike!

Jessica
the Jazz Fairy

Saskia
the Salsa Fairy

Fun-loving Saskia brings every celebration to life with her super-cool Latin dance! But with her dance ribbon missing, the girls were worried that the Wetherbury Fiesta would be a disaster...

Dance Fairies

Imogen
the Ice Dance Fairy

This icy adventure starred seven ice-skating goblins! The pesky creatures caused chaos at the Glacier Ice Rink and ruined the show for everyone. The final dance ribbon had to be returned to Imogen, before any more disasters took place.

Did you know?

Ice dance is a form of figure skating. It's been part of the Winter Olympics since 1924.

Helena
the Horseriding Fairy

It's time once again for the games to start, But with seven things lost, no one can take part!

Rachel and Kirsty were about to go horseriding when they were magically whisked to Fairyland and introduced to seven new fairy friends! The Sporty Fairies were in trouble – Jack Frost's goblins had stolen the seven magical sporty objects. With these missing, the Fairy Olympics couldn't begin, and no one could enjoy any sports!

Rainbow Reveal

The Fairy Olympics are held in the Fairyland Arena, a magical place that changes to suit whichever sport is being played!

Rainbow Reveal

The winner of the Fairy Olympics is awarded a magnificent golden cup full of luck. Jack Frost really wants to get his hands on this!

Sporty Fairies

Francesca
the Football Fairy

In Francesca's story, the girls went to watch a Tippington Rovers football match with Rachel's mum and dad! But some naughty goblins were also at the football ground, and they had Francesca's magic football…

Rainbow Reveal
In the USA, football is known as soccer!

Zoe
the Skating Fairy

With Zoe's magic shoelace missing, all skaters and skateboarders were in trouble! In this exciting adventure, it was up to the girls to help find the lace. Then Zoe could make skating fun again!

Rainbow Reveal
There is a sport called roller derby, where two teams skate round a rink together, and try to score points!

Naomi
the Netball Fairy

Netball is normally a fun and popular team sport, but with Naomi's magic netball missing, nobody was having a good time! Whilst helping Naomi, Rachel and Kirsty met a team called 'The Mean Green Netball Team'. The girls were very suspicious! Green normally means goblins, and goblins mean trouble...

Did you know?

Netball is similar to basketball in many ways, and it is thought to have developed from basketball!

Sporty Fairies

Samantha
the Swimming Fairy

Swimming is the perfect sport to enjoy on a summer day! But with Samantha's magic goggles missing, Kirsty and Rachel had to be on high alert when they went for a dip at Aqua World!

Alice
the Tennis Fairy

In Alice's exciting story, Tippington Tennis Club was taken over by troops of tennis-playing goblins! Rachel and Kirsty had the tricky task of helping Alice to get her magic racquet back.

Gemma
the Gymnastics Fairy

By the time Kirsty and Rachel met Gemma properly, it was almost time for the Fairy Olympics to begin! Gemma's magic hoop was missing, and had to be returned to Fairyland – otherwise Jack Frost and his goblins could still win the games and cause lots of trouble with the golden Fairyland Olympics Cup.

Did you know?

The word gymnastics comes from an ancient Greek word meaning 'to exercise'.

Rainbow Reveal

Gemma loves her magic hoop. She likes to entertain her Sporty Fairies friends by spinning it round and round and performing lots of tricks, without the hoop ever touching the floor!

Rainbow Reveal

The Sporty Fairies are trying to teach the goblins a very important lesson – you don't have to cheat to enjoy sport!

Sporty Fairies

Poppy
the Piano Fairy

The magical instruments
must be found,
For without them all music
makes a horrid sound!

Kirsty and Rachel love listening to music! So they were shocked to learn that music everywhere could be ruined because Jack Frost had stolen all of the magic musical instruments from the Royal School of Music. In Poppy's story, the Ice Lord formed a band with his goblins and was going to enter a music contest in the human world. The girls had to stop him!

Did you know?

There are 88 keys on a standard piano. Of these, 52 are white and 36 are black.

Rainbow Reveal

Jack Frost's group, Frosty's Gobolicious Band, play at the goblin party in Elizabeth the Jubilee Fairy's story.

Ellie
the Guitar Fairy

Ellie just loves playing funky tunes on her electric guitar! But when it was in the hands of the naughty goblins in the human world, even she couldn't play a note without it sounding awful…

Rainbow Reveal
There are two main types of guitar: acoustic and electric.

Rainbow Reveal
The enchanting music that comes from Fiona's flute makes people want to follow it!

Fiona
the Flute Fairy

Fiona the Flute Fairy fluttered magically out of a sparkly card at the start of this story! She knew her magic flute was nearby, but had to ask for help from Rachel and Kirsty so she could get it back before the goblins caused more trouble.

Music Fairies

Danni
the Drum Fairy

Rainbow Reveal
The Music Fairies' instruments are still fairy size in the human world, so they can be very hard to spot!

Rachel and Kirsty were going to star in a pop video in this story! They were so excited but they also knew they had to stay alert if they were to find another missing magical musical instrument. Luckily the silly goblins soon appeared with Danni's magic drumsticks…

Rainbow Reveal
Whenever Danni uses her wand, lots of tiny drumsticks appear!

Rainbow Reveal
Danni the Drum Fairy is the only fairy not holding her wand on her book cover!

Maya
the Harp Fairy

Maya's elegant harp plays magical musical melodies! But with the magic harp missing, harp music everywhere sounded awful. Rachel and Kirsty had to help Maya find her instrument before their friend's wedding was totally ruined…

Victoria
the Violin Fairy

The girls had a sneak peek at Frosty's Gobolicious Band in this fairy tale! With Victoria's magic violin nearby to keep them in harmony, the band sounded great. But the girls had to return the violin to Victoria so all music could be harmonious.

Music Fairies

Sadie
the Saxophone Fairy

Sadie's story was the final Music Fairies adventure, and it was time for the National Talent Competition! With Sadie's saxophone missing, the girls knew that Frosty's Gobolicious Band could easily win the competition, putting Fairyland in danger. Kirsty and Rachel had to work hard and save the day, to prevent the competition being ruined for everyone!

Did you know?
The saxophone is made in about eight different sizes. That's not including fairy size!

Did you know?
Most saxophones are made from brass!

Rainbow Reveal
Even when the talent competition is over, Jack Frost still thinks he is a super-talented pop star!

Ashley
the Dragon Fairy

The magical animals are lost in our world. They really need help from two special girls!

Rainbow Reveal
Ashley's young dragon is called Sizzle. He looks after the magical power of imagination.

Rachel and Kirsty were away for a week at an outdoor adventure camp when they met the Magical Animal Fairies. They discovered that Jack Frost had stolen seven young magical animals. The baby animals were all being trained to use a particular type of magic, so they could help everyone enjoy life. The animals escaped Jack Frost's icy clutches – but then got lost in the human world!

Rainbow Reveal
When Sizzle sneezes, small flames appear. All of Fairyland must watch out when the baby dragon has a cold!

Rainbow Reveal
Ashley has a Chinese dragon on the leg of her combats. This type of dragon is said to ward off evil spirits!

Magical Animal Fairies

Lara
the Black Cat Fairy

During a camp activity, Rachel and Kirsty found Lara's magical animal. Lucky, an adorable little black cat, has the power to bring good luck. But as bad luck was happening everywhere, the girls did their best to get the pretty kitty back to Lara.

Erin
the Firebird Fairy

In Erin's adventure, the girls spotted a very unusual bird by the stream! It was Giggles the firebird, whose magic looks after humour. Rachel, Kirsty and Erin had to try and reach Giggles before the goblins got hold of him.

Rihanna
the Seahorse Fairy

Rihanna's magic seahorse, Bubbles, looks after friendship – which is very important to both fairies and humans! When Bubbles isn't in Fairyland with his fairy keeper, friendships everywhere suffer. So when Jack Frost stole Bubbles, Rachel and Kirsty had to find the little seahorse and reunite him with Rihanna.

Did you know?
Seahorse babies are born from the dads, not the mums!

Did you know?
Normally seahorses live in certain oceans, but as Bubbles is a magic seahorse, he can swim in lakes and rivers, too!

Rainbow Reveal
Rihanna's magic allows the girls to breathe underwater!

Magical Animal Fairies

59

Sophia
the Snow Swan Fairy

The girls were on a night-time walk at camp when a shimmering swan caught their eye! They had to cross a beautiful waterfall and reach Sophia's baby swan, Belle, before the goblins did.

Rainbow Reveal
Sophia's magic power is to spread compassion.

Leona
the Unicorn Fairy

Leona's magical animal is Twisty the baby unicorn – he looks like a white pony! Twisty's magic came in very handy when Rachel's wrist was hurt by the actions of a careless goblin.

Rainbow Reveal
Leona and Helena the Horseriding Fairy spend hours plaiting the manes of their horsey friends!

Caitlin
the Ice Bear Fairy

Rainbow
Reveal
Mean Jack Frost stole
the Magical Animals
because he knew the world
would be a miserable place
without them.

I t was a chilly final day at the adventure camp and the girls had a big hill to climb! From the top of the hill they were hoping to spot the final missing magical animal, Crystal the ice bear cub. But Jack Frost was also nearby with his frosty magic, hoping to find the little bear first…

Did you know?

A polar bear's fur isn't white! Each hair is a hollow tube that reflects light. It also traps the sun's heat to help keep the polar bear warm.

Magical Animal Fairies

Nicole
the Beach Fairy

These seven fairies keep the world clean, Safe from the Ice Lord, who's nasty and mean!

In the Green Fairies' adventures, Rachel and Kirsty asked the fairies for *their* help! They returned to Rainspell Island for a holiday and were very upset to see that the beautiful beach was covered in litter. They knew they needed some magic to help them clean up the environment and show others how to do the same. But the last thing Jack Frost wanted was more interfering fairies…

Rainbow Reveal
At the start of these seven stories, the Green Fairies are still in training!

Rainbow Reveal
The goblins steal the Green Fairies' wands. Without them the fairies can only do a certain amount to help the planet.

Isabella
the Air Fairy

It's Isabella's job to make sure that the air humans and fairies breathe is as clean as possible! In her adventure, Isabella asked Rachel and Kirsty to help her clean up Seabury's air.

Edie
the Garden Fairy

Gardens are such important places! They provide safe homes for lots of wildlife and plants. When Rachel and Kirsty met Edie, they all volunteered to create a special garden. But Jack Frost had other plans…

Green Fairies

Coral
the Reef Fairy

Coral joined the girls for a wonderful underwater adventure in this story! The girls magically travelled to a warm, tropical ocean many hundreds of miles away from Rainspell Island. They had to help Coral teach an important lesson to some very destructive goblins.

Rainbow Reveal
Coral's emerald ankle bracelets were a birthday gift from the Jewel Fairies.

Did you know?
Every coral reef is a living organism! Reefs are very delicate and easily damaged by human touch or polluted water.

The world's biggest reef is the Great Barrier Reef in Australia. It is so long it can be seen from space!

Lily
the Rainforest Fairy

The girls were on a nature walk on Rainspell Island when, with the help of Lily's fairy magic, they were whisked to an exotic rainforest. They met a host of amazing exotic creatures!

Milly
the River Fairy

Milly had to get her wand back from Jack Frost so she could make all rivers clean and healthy once more. But first she needed the girls to help her outwit the goblins…

Rainbow Reveal
Milly and Hayley the Rain Fairy are the very best of friends. These water-loving fairies love to splash around in rivers and puddles!

Green Fairies

Carrie
the Snow Cap Fairy

Carrie's adventure was the last in the Green Fairies series! Rachel and Kirsty had only one wand left to find but Jack Frost was determined to hang onto it, leading to a showdown amongst the polar ice caps. Carrie and the girls had to convince the Ice Lord to return the wand and save Earth.

Rainbow Reveal
Carrie and Crystal the Snow Fairy have friendly competitions to see who can create the biggest and most sparkly snowballs!

Rainbow Reveal
Carrie's jacket is fake fur – she loves animals too much to wear real fur!

Did you know?

The temperature at the South Pole can go as low as -65 degrees Celsius. Brrr!

Ally
the Dolphin Fairy

These fairies care for oceans with the Magical Shell, They must find the missing pieces for all to be well!

The girls were at the start of a seaside holiday when they received a magical invitation to the Fairyland Ocean Gala! They learned that Shannon the Ocean Fairy plays a magical tune on the Golden Conch Shell each year to make everything harmonious in all the oceans. But Jack Frost's clumsy goblins had stolen the shell and broken it into pieces. The Ocean Fairies needed Rachel and Kirsty's help!

Rainbow Reveal
Each of the seven Ocean Fairies has an ocean animal as a companion. These animals lead each fairy to a piece of the Golden Conch Shell!

Did you know?
Dolphins live in groups called pods. Sometimes these pods can contain several hundred dolphins!

Ocean Fairies

Amelie
the Seal Fairy

A magical, sparkly light in a lantern led Rachel and Kirsty to Amelie! This little fairy knew her seal, Silky, was nearby, which meant the shell piece was close by, too. But so were some goblins dressed as pirates…

Did you know?

You can find seals in the UK! They are shy creatures and like quiet areas where they can sunbathe.

Pia
the Penguin Fairy

Pia took the girls on a wintry trip to the South Pole! But the girls found that everything was topsy-turvy because the conch shell hadn't been played. Even animals that live near the sea, such as polar bears, were very confused and in the wrong place!

Did you know?

Penguins are birds, but they can't fly!

Tess
the Sea Turtle Fairy

Rainbow
Reveal

The silly goblins think that baby turtles are baby Pogwurzels!

Rainbow
Reveal

When Tess waves her wand, lots of tiny turtles appear!

A tropical island was the setting for this fairy adventure! Tess knew that her ocean animal, a beautiful turtle called Pearl, was near the fourth piece of the missing conch shell. Rachel and Kirsty had to help get the shell piece back to Fairyland so that the chaos in the ocean could be put right. But first they had to help hundreds of baby turtles and deal with three very scared goblins!

Did you know?

Mummy turtles lay their eggs on beaches and bury them in the sand. When the babies hatch, the clever baby turtles head straight into the sea!

Ocean Fairies

69

Stephanie
the Starfish Fairy

In this story, it was time for the girls to enjoy a spot of stargazing. But there was only one star the girls wanted to spot – Stephanie's magical starfish, Spike!

Did you know?
There are thought to be 2,000 different species of starfish on Earth!

Whitney
the Whale Fairy

Rainbow Reveal
Whitney and Flukey patrol the seas making sure every whale is safe and happy.

Ahoy there! Rachel and Kirsty were on board an old-fashioned sailing ship when they helped Whitney. There was lots to see, including a pod of killer whales! One of the whales looked strangely sparkly, so the girls knew that a missing piece of the magical shell was close by…

Courtney
the Clownfish Fairy

Did you know?
Clownfish are really small! The biggest they can grow is 18 centimetres long.

It was almost time for Rachel and Kirsty's holiday to end when they met Courtney and her clownfish, Tickle. They visited a magical underwater funfair, but Jack Frost and lots of goblins were also at the fair searching for the Golden Conch Shell!

Rainbow Reveal
When Courtney appears in the story, she's inside a fish-shaped balloon!

Rainbow Reveal
At the end of their ocean adventures the girls are given a beautiful conch shell as a gift from Queen Titania and King Oberon.

Ocean Fairies

71

Ava
the Sunset Fairy

We all know that night follows day, And these fairies make night special in every way.

The Twilight Fairies have such a special job, using their magic fairy dust to make make sure that everything is looked after between dusk and dawn. Kirsty and Rachel were visiting Camp Stargaze for a week with their families when they spotted a very strange green sunset…they just knew it was to do with Jack Frost! First of all they had to help Ava find her missing bag of sunbeam dust.

Rainbow Reveal

If it weren't for Ava's sunbeam dust, there would be night-time chaos everywhere!

Did you know?

Sometimes you see the brightest sunsets in a city. When the air is full of particles of dust and dirt, these particles reflect light in all directions.

Lexi
the Firefly Fairy

The girls went on a night-time stroll to the twinkling tree in this story, but with Lexi's bag of magic twilight dust missing, the twinkling tree was not living up to its name…

Did you know?
Fireflies are also known as 'lightning bugs' because of the flashes of light they produce!

Zara
the Starlight Fairy

Rachel and Kirsty spotted a strange constellation in Camp Stargaze's observatory at the start of this story! With Zara's bag of star dust missing, the stars were up to all sorts of odd things…

Did you know?
A constellation is a group of stars that look like a dot-to-dot puzzle!

Twilight Fairies

73

Morgan
the Midnight Fairy

Rainbow
Reveal
In this story, the goblins are having an amazing feast of their own with the help of Morgan's magic fairy dust.

Some of the best parties are held at midnight, and Morgan makes sure they are always exciting with the help of her enchanted night dust. But when her magical dust went missing, everything started to go wrong. The fire wouldn't light, the marshmallows wouldn't roast and the midnight stories all had the wrong endings!

Did you know?

Midnight falls at 12 o'clock each night. Most people are fast asleep at this time of night!

Rainbow
Reveal
Morgan's dress is the colour of the night sky at midnight!

Yasmin
the Night Owl Fairy

All sorts of animals are awake at night-time, but with Yasmin's magic bag of sleep dust missing, the behaviour of night-time and daytime animals went all topsy-turvy!

Maisie
the Moonbeam Fairy

Moonlight is the most magical of lights, but in Maisie's story the silly goblins tried to make their own moon! It was up to the girls and Maisie to stop them and return Maisie's moon dust to her.

Rainbow Reveal
Without Maisie's moon dust, even the fairies sleep all day!

Twilight Fairies

Sabrina
the Sweet Dreams Fairy

Everybody dreams, even Jack Frost and the goblins!

Sabrina has such an important job – she makes sure that everyone has sweet dreams rather than nightmares! But she needs her magical dream dust to do this. Once, her bag fell into the hands of the goblins, and nobody in the human world or Fairyland could sleep peacefully!

ZZZ
ZZZ
ZZZ

Rainbow Reveal
Sabrina sometimes sings a lovely lullaby that puts everyone to sleep!

Rainbow Reveal
Without her dream dust, Sabrina has been known to sleep-fly!

Rainbow Reveal
A nightmare is a bad dream. Sabrina's magical dream dust makes sure everyone's dreams are lovely and fun!

Madison
the Magic Show Fairy

All in Fairyland
love to go,
To see these fairies'
amazing shows!

It was October half term and almost time for the Tippington Variety Show when the girls met Madison! They were really looking forward to watching all the different acts practise and perform. But when the girls discovered that Madison's wand had been stolen, they knew the variety show would be lacking some very important magic…

Rainbow Reveal
Madison loves performing all magic tricks, but her favourite is making a pack of cards float up into the air!

Rainbow Reveal
The Showtime Fairies' magic stars help everyone to make the most of their special skill or talent.

Showtime Fairies

Leah
the Theatre Fairy

Rachel's school was rehearsing for a performance of Cinderella in the beautiful Swan Theatre in Leah's story! The school was hoping to get to the finals of the Tippington Variety Show. But everything was going wrong because of Leah's missing star…

Did you know?

The most famous fairy in theatre is Shakespeare's Queen Titania.

Alesha
the Acrobat Fairy

It's Alesha's job to make sure that everyone taking part in acrobatic shows performs well and has lots of fun. But this can only happen when she has her magic star…

Rainbow Reveal
Alesha's bright pink leotard has magical fairy dust sewn into it!

Darcey
the Dance Diva Fairy

The girls visited the Funky Feet dance studio in this story! Rachel's school was auditioning for a place in the Tippington Variety Show with an amazing hip-hop dance routine. But, with Darcey's star missing, there was nothing amazing about it, and all the other schools' routines were going horribly wrong, too!

Rainbow Reveal
Darcey and the Dance Fairies often get together to perform lots of different dances for their fairy friends.

Rainbow Reveal
Jack Frost wanted the goblins to hide the magic stars in the human world so that nobody showed any talents.

Rainbow Reveal
Darcey's stunning dress is in the style of the 1920s! The fringes sway and shake when she dances.

Showtime Fairies

Amelia
the Singing Fairy

Amelia's magic star allows true singing talent to shine, but when it fell into the hands of the goblins everything went topsy-turvy and the pesky creatures had all the singing talent instead!

Rainbow Reveal
Amelia's beautiful pendant glows when she sings and bathes her in a magical light!

Isla
the Ice Star Fairy

Ice-skating is such a special skill and practice really does make perfect! But no matter how much the competitors rehearsed in this story, their routines weren't getting any better. The girls knew they had to find Isla's magic star!

Rainbow Reveal
Imogen the Ice Dance Fairy and Isla love to dance duets on the ice!

Taylor
the Talent Show Fairy

I n Taylor's tale, it was time for the Tippington Variety Show to begin. Jack Frost came to the show personally to make sure that Taylor's magic star wasn't returned to her. Her star makes sure shows run smoothly, and Jack Frost wanted to ruin the show for everyone!

Rainbow Reveal
The Showtime Fairies have help from the Dance Fairies and Music Fairies to perfect their talents.

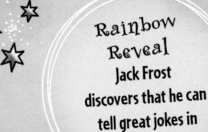

Rainbow Reveal
Jack Frost discovers that he can tell great jokes in this story!

Rainbow Reveal
Everyone is really good at something, whether it's singing a song, drawing a picture or telling a joke. Why don't you and your friends have a talent show? You'll all be winners!

Showtime Fairies

Honor
the Happy Days Fairy

Rachel and Kirsty are invited to a ball, But Jack Frost tries to ruin it all!

Rachel and Kirsty were spending a week at Golden Palace when they met the Princess Fairies. It's a magical old castle where real princes and princesses once lived! The girls were whisked away to a Fairyland Ball by Polly the Party Fun Fairy. But mean Jack Frost gate-crashed the ball and stole the royal fairies' tiaras! Without the tiaras, no human or fairy would ever have a happy time again.

Rainbow Reveal
The Queen's magic sent the missing tiaras to Golden Palace.

Did you know?
The oldest castle in England is the Tower of London, where the girls meet Elizabeth the Jubilee Fairy!

Demi
the Dressing-Up Fairy

The girls and their friends enjoyed exploring Golden Palace in Demi's story – but they soon had to help Demi find her tiara, so everyone could look beautiful at the pageant.

Anya
the Cuddly Creatures Fairy

Golden Palace has its own petting zoo and there are lots of different animals to meet there! But with Anya's golden tiara in the hands of the goblins, all the cuddly creatures behave very oddly…

Rainbow Reveal

Anya's magic helps keep the special friendship between animals and humans strong.

Princess Fairies

Elisa
the Adventure Fairy

Rainbow Reveal

Each of the Princess Fairies' tiaras has a different-shaped jewel.

With Elisa's sparkly tiara missing, nobody wanted to have any fun! The girls had to track down the goblins to put things right. In this story, everyone apart from Rachel and Kirsty lost their sense of adventure.

Rainbow Reveal

Elisa often organises trips and treasure hunts for her fairy friends.

Rainbow Reveal

Elisa and Maddie once used their combined magic to make a brilliant adventure playground for all their fairy friends to enjoy.

Rainbow Reveal

Elisa's magic makes the spirit of fun and adventure strong in every human and fairy.

Lizzie
the Sweet Treats Fairy

I t was time for a royal tea party at Golden Palace and everyone was looking forward to having lots of delicious things to eat. But without Princess Lizzie's golden tiara to make sure everything tasted yummy, all of the sweet treats were sure to be awful!

Rainbow Reveal
Lizzie often swaps recipes with Cherry the Cake Fairy and Honey the Sweet Fairy. Yummy!

Maddie
the Playtime Fairy

M addie the Playtime Fairy makes sure that children everywhere enjoy games and playtime! But with her magic tiara missing, everyone at Golden Palace was very miserable. Rachel and Kirsty had to find the tiara before the sports day was ruined!

Rainbow Reveal
Maddie is riding a rocking horse when the girls discover her!

Princess Fairies

Eva
the Enchanted Ball Fairy

Eva's special magic makes sure that everyone is beautifully dressed for important parties and balls. But whilst Eva's tiara is with Jack Frost, celebrations everywhere will be a disaster. In this story Rachel and Kirsty had to visit the scary Ice Castle, to take Eva's tiara back from the Ice Lord!

Rainbow Reveal
Rachel and Kirsty enjoy two wonderful balls – one at Golden Palace and the other at the Fairyland Palace.

Rainbow Reveal
Jack Frost is such a troublemaker that the fairies have stopped inviting him to their parties!

Rainbow Reveal
Ella looks after enchanted balls but King Oberon and Queen Titania also host masquerade balls where everyone wears masks! Sometimes it's very hard to tell who is who.

Jessie
the Lyrics Fairy

The girls were so excited to return to Rainspell Island for a five-day music festival! But when they got there, they found out that mean Jack Frost had stolen the Pop Star Fairies' magical clef necklaces. Without Jessie's necklace, none of the stars singing at pop events anywhere would remember their words!

Rainbow Reveal
Jessie loves using her imagination to write song lyrics.

Did you know?
Song lyrics are like a poem or a story set to music!

Rainbow Reveal
Jessie's pink boots were a present from Phoebe the Fashion Fairy.

Pop Star Fairies

Adele
the Singing Coach Fairy

Adele's magic helps pop stars in Fairyland and the human world sing on key! But with her magic necklace missing, no one could strike the right notes at the music festival. Well, apart from a mysterious new pop star called Gobby…

Rainbow Reveal
In Adele's story the girls get to meet their favourite ever boy band, A-OK!

Vanessa
the Dance Steps Fairy

Being able to dance is a very important part of being a pop star! Vanessa helps each star perfect their routines. In her story, it was almost time for pop sensation Sasha Sharp to perform, but Sasha couldn't dance a single step!

Rainbow Reveal
Vanessa's blue playsuit was handmade by Tyra the Dress Designer Fairy.

Miley
the Stylist Fairy

Miley's magic helps pop stars look their very best. But at the Rainspell Festival, Miley's necklace went missing, so all the pop stars' clothes and accessories were in a terrible mess…

Rainbow Reveal
Miley is always on the lookout for the hottest new trend.

Did you know?

Fashion stylists select clothing for TV ads and magazine pictures, as well as for pop performances!

Rainbow Reveal
Jack Frost thinks he knows everything about fashion – take a peek at the Fashion Fairies books to find out more!

Rainbow Reveal
Miley's top style tip is to wear a bright scarf – it can quickly update any outfit! You can wear it as a belt, tied loosely around your neck or thrown casually around your shoulders.

Pop Star Fairies

Frankie
the Make-Up Fairy

Having your face painted at a festival is always great fun. But when Frankie's necklace went missing at the Rainspell event, all face paint and make-up looked horrible!

Rainbow Reveal
Frankie was in the same class at school as Miranda the Beauty Fairy.

Rochelle
the Star Spotter Fairy

Rainbow Reveal
Taylor the Talent Show Fairy shares her secret talent-spotting tips with Rochelle.

Rochelle's skill is very special to all pop sensations – she spots new stars and makes sure that every one of them feels full of confidence. But with her magical clef in the hands of the goblins at the Rainspell Festival, the search for new talent seemed to be over… until the girls saved the day!

Una
the Concert Fairy

Una's magic clef necklace makes sure concerts run smoothly, so with it missing, the final concert of the Rainspell Music Festival went horribly wrong... The girls had to trick Jack Frost into returning the necklace so there could be a fabulous festival finale!

Rainbow Reveal
A magical music festival takes place in Fairyland at the same time as the Rainspell Music Festival!

Rainbow Reveal
Una loves orange chocolate-chip cookies.

Rainbow Reveal
Jack Frost's stage name is Jax Tempo.

Rainbow Reveal
Sometimes Una feels a bit nervous before she goes on stage in front of lots of other fairies! But her fairy friends always make her feel better.

Pop Star Fairies

Miranda
the Beauty Fairy

These fairies make fashion feel trendy and new. They help natural beauty to shine brightly through!

When a brand-new shopping centre opened in Tippington, Kirsty and Rachel decided to enter a charity fashion show where they could design their own clothes. But mean Jack Frost was up to his old tricks again. He thought everyone in the world should dress like him, so he stole the seven Fashion Fairies' magical items – including Miranda's shimmery magical lipstick – to put his plan into action!

Nail Varnish

Did you know?

Queen Elizabeth II has her own special lipstick called The Balmoral Lipstick. It was made to match her coronation robes.

Rainbow Reveal
Although Miranda loves to experiment with different make-up, she knows that natural beauty should always shine through.

Rainbow Reveal
Miranda has over 100 lipsticks in her make-up collection!

Claudia
the Accessories Fairy

It's lovely to have a pretty accessory to match an outfit! But with Claudia's magic necklace in the hands of Jack Frost and his goblins, accessories everywhere fell apart and lost their sparkle…

Rainbow Reveal
Claudia always matches her hairband to her shoes!

Tyra
the Dress Designer Fairy

Rainbow Reveal
Tyra likes to design new dresses with Miley the Stylist Fairy!

In Tyra's story, it was time for the girls to get creative at the Design-and-Make workshop! But with Tyra's magical tape measure missing, all the clothes in the Tippington Fountains Shopping Centre were falling apart!

Fashion Fairies

Matilda
the Hair Stylist Fairy

When your hair has been styled nicely, it makes you feel very special! But without Matilda's special magic, scissors get blunt and in this story, everyone's hair turned a strange shade of blue!

Rainbow Reveal

Matilda's top haircare tip is to keep your locks clean and knot-free!

Brooke
the Photographer Fairy

Rachel and Kirsty were taking part in a fashion photoshoot when Brooke appeared! Brooke's magic camera was missing, and when Jack Frost started acting like a stroppy model, the girls had a suspicion where the camera might be...

Rainbow Reveal

Brooke's hobby is to cut up photos she's taken, and make them into collages for her friends!

Alexa
the Fashion Reporter Fairy

Jack Frost was determined to let everyone know about his crazy new fashion label, Ice Blue, and he used the magic of Alexa's stolen pen to do it! The girls had to track down the missing magical item to stop Jack Frost from becoming the most famous fashion designer in the human world.

Rainbow Reveal
Alexa and Hannah the Happy Ever After Fairy both use their magical pens to write stories for the Fairyland News.

Did you know?

The most famous fashion magazine is called *Vogue*.

Rainbow Reveal
Jack Frost is so silly and vain that in Alexa's story he interviews himself about his own fashion label!

Fashion Fairies

95

Lola
the Fashion Show Fairy

In this final Fashion Fairy adventure, it was time for the Tippington Fountains fashion show! Kirsty and Rachel couldn't wait to be part of the fun and model their own designs on the catwalk. But Lola's magical backstage pass went missing, and the girls knew that without it, the fashion show would be a spectacular disaster!

Rainbow Reveal
Lola's sparkly silver boots are perfect for a night out dancing with Jade the Disco Fairy!

Rainbow Reveal
Jack Frost almost ruined the final fashion show for everyone! He wanted to be the star of the show.

Did you know?
Each year designers hold big fashion shows in New York, Paris, Milan and London to showcase the next season's designs.

Lottie
the Lollipop Fairy

The Sweet Fairies make delicious treats That everybody loves to eat!

Lovely Lottie the Lollipop Fairy is the first Sweet Fairy that Kirsty and Rachel helped! Honey the Sweet Fairy whisked the girls away to Fairyland and introduced her to Lottie and her friends. Jack Frost stole all of the Sweet Fairies' magic charms and gave them to his goblin servants to hide in the human world. The girls had to return the charms to stop sweet treats tasting awful forever and ever!

Rainbow Reveal
Lottie's dress is a real POP of candy colours, including hot pink, lime green and pretty purple! She accessorises her divine dress with a simple pair of wedges. Fashion perfection!

Rainbow Reveal
Wetherbury village has a sweet shop looked after by Mrs Twist. But when the Sweet Fairies' charms went missing, all her sweets and chocolate started to taste yucky...

Sweet Fairies

Esme
the Ice Cream Fairy

Did you know?

Jack Frost wanted to build a special Candy Castle! He even wanted to fill a whole swimming pool with sticky melted ice cream. Yuck!

Esme the Ice Cream Fairy's special ice cream charm helps her to make this treat super tasty. But when the goblins got their sticky mitts on the charm, they started making the yummiest, greenest ice cream in town!

Rainbow Reveal

Esme loves all the different flavours of ice cream, but her number one favourite is a vanilla and strawberry cone sprinkled with chocolate chips. Delicious!

Did you know?

Ice cream has been around for many hundreds of years and it's enjoyed all over the world. How many different flavours can you think of?

Coco
the Cupcake Fairy

With Coco's magic charm missing, Kirsty and Rachel found it very difficult to make special birthday cupcakes…

Clara
the Chocolate Fairy

In this adventure, Rachel and Kirsty visited Jack Frost's brand new Candy Castle to find Clara's magic cocoa bean charm.

Sweet Fairies

Madeleine
the Cookie Fairy

Madeleine's magical cookie cutter charm was lost somewhere in the Candy Land factory! The girls had to help her to get it back before all the cookies turned to cookie crumbs…

Layla
the Candyfloss Fairy

Candyfloss is often eaten at fairs and in this book, Wetherbury Funfair was the perfect place to track down Layla's magic charm…

Nina
the Birthday Cake Fairy

Rainbow Reveal
Jack Frost made his goblins build him a HUGE castle out of delicious sweets and treats. But the creatures are so greedy that they couldn't stop themselves from eating it!

Rainbow Reveal
The baskets of sweet treats delivered to all the fairies contains cookies, chocolates, muffins and sweets. Yummy!

Did you know?
Birthdays have been celebrated with a cake for many hundreds of years. Some people say that the tradition dates back to Roman times.

In this adventure it was Kirsty's birthday and Rachel threw her an amazing surprise birthday party! But with Nina's magic charm missing, there was no birthday cake to enjoy. The girls had to visit Jack Frost's Candy Castle to find the birthday candle charm. But Jack Frost was determined to keep hold of it… and eat all of the birthday cake!

Sweet Fairies

Mae
the Panda Fairy

Mae the Panda Fairy is the first Baby Animal Rescue Fairy that the girls meet! Kirsty and Rachel were helping out at the Wild Woods Nature Reserve for a week when they were whisked to Fairyland and visited the magical Fairyland Reserve.

Rainbow Reveal
In this adventure, for the girls to be able to help Mae rescue a special baby panda, Kirsty and Rachel were magically transported to the mountains of China!

Rainbow Reveal
Kirsty and Rachel LOVE animals and in this set of adventures, they are able to talk to all animals, and understand every word that any animal says. Truly magical!

Did you know?
There aren't very many pandas left in the wild, so it's very important that we all do our best to look after them all, just like Mae does!

Kitty
the Tiger Fairy

In this amazing story Kirsty and Rachel were turned into fairies and met THREE adorable tiger cubs in an exotic jungle! But could they stop the naughty goblins from taking the precious cubs away from their home…?

Mara
the Meerkat Fairy

Rachel and Kirsty love meerkats and so they were very excited to meet Mara and a whole host of adorable furry friends in this adventure! But could they trick the goblins and stop them from taking a poor meerkat back to Jack Frost's icy castle?

Baby Animal Rescue Fairies

Savannah
the Zebra Fairy

Rainbow Reveal
When Savannah first met Rachel and Kirsty, her stripy top blended in perfectly with the stripes on Kirsty's hat!

In this story Kirsty and Rachel travelled to the grassy plains to help Ziggy the zebra foal! The goblins had made some horrid traps and were determined to take the little zebra back to Jack Frost's icy domain.

Kimberley
the Koala Fairy

In the human world, Kimberly's koala pals only live in one place: amazing Australia! Jack Frost's goblins travelled there and took Kiki the koala away from her family. Could the girls and Kimberley take her home…?

Rainbow Reveal
In this set of adventures, Kirsty and Rachel are helping out at the Wild Woods Nature Reserve.

Rosie
the Honey Bear Fairy

In this adventure Kirsty and Rachel were so pleased to meet up with an old friend, Queenie the bee! She helped them to find an adorable baby brown bear called Billy. The friends knew that Billy's disappearance had something to do with some very suspicious green hikers who were making a lot of noise…

Rainbow Reveal
There are lots of different bears in the world and Rosie makes sure that they are all happy and looked after.

Did you know?
Brown bears hibernate during the long cold months, which means they go into a very deep sleep. They can hibernate for up to seven months of the year. Yawn!

Rainbow Reveal
Brown bears love the taste of sweet honey, but they also eat lots of other things including grass, plants, insects and fish.

Baby Animal Rescue Fairies

Anna
the Arctic Fox Fairy

This adventure started with the girls going on a magical night walk at the Wild Woods Nature Reserve. But their walk was cut short when they met Anna and were whisked away to one of the coldest places on Earth: the Arctic!

Rainbow Reveal

When the girls and Anna were searching for Dazzle, the missing Arctic fox cub, they bumped into Jack Frost! He was determined to take Dazzle back to the zoo at his Ice Castle...

Rainbow Reveal

On their Arctic adventure, Kirsty and Rachel were able to help a husky called Shika with a poorly paw. They could understand everything she was saying thanks to the special magic given to them by their fairy friends.

Did you know?

The Arctic fox's coat changes with the seasons, so it is white in the winter when it's snowy everywhere and then it changes to brown or grey when the snow melts in spring or summer!

Kayla
the Pottery Fairy

These clever fairies
make and do,
Magical crafts for
me and you!

Rainbow Reveal

The goblins were
having lots of fun at the pottery
class on Rainspell Island.
Unfortunately their idea of fun
was to throw lots of clay
around, making
a terrible mess!

Rainbow Reveal

Kayla's magical object is
a beautiful vase. A haze of
shimmering sparkles
surrounds it.

In this story Rachel and Kirsty returned to Rainspell Island, where their amazing fairy adventures began! The girls were looking forward to enjoying Crafts Week, but soon Kayla whisked them away to Fairyland where a Magical Crafts Week was taking place…

Magical Crafts Fairies

Annabelle
the Drawing Fairy

Kirsty and Rachel love drawing, and they were looking forward to picking up some top tips during Crafts Week! But with Annabelle's magical pencil sharpener missing, it seemed everyone's drawing skills would get worse, not better.

Zadie
the Sewing Fairy

As soon as Kirsty's mum had problems threading a needle, the girls knew that they had to help Zadie find her magical thimble!

Josie
the Jewellery-Making Fairy

Making jewellery is a really special skill, and Rachel and Kirsty can't wait to learn how to make their own accessories! But they know that if they can't return Josie's beaded ribbon, all jewels will be broken and tarnished forever.

Rainbow Reveal

All fairies can talk to animals and in this adventure, Josie asks a very friendly seagull for his help!

Did you know?

A friendship bracelet is a great gift to give someone. These are easy to make and you can use lots of different colours.

Rainbow Reveal

It turns out that the goblins like to wear lots of jewellery at the same time! In this story they wear lots of noisy beads.

Magical Crafts Fairies

109

Violet
the Painting Fairy

Painting should be lots of fun, but in this adventure all the colours were mixed-up and yucky because of Violet's missing paintbrush! The only person in the art class who had perfect painting skills was a tall, icy-blue person with very spiky hair…

Rainbow Reveal
The Rainbow Magic Fairies always appear to the girls in wonderful ways and in this book Violet appeared in a painting. Magical!

Rainbow Reveal
Violet is always ready for painting fun in her pretty but practical outfit! She wears cool denim dungarees and a cropped top.

Did you know?
One of the most famous paintings of all time is a picture of a woman called the Mona Lisa. It was painted by Leonardo da Vinci hundreds of years ago.

Libby
the Story-Writing Fairy

Libby loves writing stories, and her magic helps everyone to enjoy books. But when her magical notebook is stolen, nobody can write stories anymore and even existing stories are all muddled up!

Roxie
the Baking Fairy

It's almost the end of the Rainspell Island Crafts Week and the girls are helping to bake cakes and biscuits for the exhibition. But poor Roxie still doesn't have her magical cookie cutter. Without this, all baking will go disastrously wrong!

Magical Crafts Fairies

Holly
the Christmas Fairy

Holly's the fairy who spreads Christmas cheer, On the happiest, most magical day of the year!

Kirsty and Rachel met Holly on a trip to Fairyland just before Christmas, when they discovered that Jack Frost had stolen Santa's sleigh! Without it, Santa couldn't deliver any presents to boys and girls in the human world. Holly needed the girls' help to find her three magical Christmas presents and put things right.

Rainbow Reveal
Holly gives Santa's reindeer flying lessons every year!

Did you know?
Santa and his reindeer travel 75.5 million miles on Christmas Eve!

Rainbow Reveal
Holly's scarlet dress was made for her by Santa's elves. It's made from the same material as Santa's robes!

Summer
the Holiday Fairy

Rachel and Kirsty were so excited to be returning to Rainspell Island for a summer holiday! But things weren't how they remembered them at all…the sea was rough, the beach wasn't sandy and even the ice cream tasted horrid! The girls had to help Summer find her Rainspell shells and make summer holidays fun for everyone once again!

Rainbow Reveal
Jack Frost stole the Rainspell shells because he didn't want anyone else to have a nice holiday.

Stella
the Star Fairy

Each year, Stella the Star Fairy uses her three magic Christmas tree decorations to make sure that everyone's Christmas is shining and bright. But when mean Jack Frost stole the magic decorations, the special time of year looked like it would be dark and miserable for everyone…

Rainbow Reveal
Stella the Star Fairy and Holly the Christmas Fairy are best friends!

Kylie
the Carnival Fairy

Sunnydays Carnival only comes to town once a year and everyone has a brilliant time going on the rides, playing games and watching the parades. But the year Rachel and Kirsty met Kylie, Jack Frost and his goblins were at the carnival too! The pesky creatures stole Kylie's three magic hats and everything started to go wrong. The girls had to move quickly and help Kylie outwit the mean Ice Lord and his goblin servants.

Did you know?

One of the biggest carnivals in the world is held each year in the Brazilian city of Rio de Janeiro. Over 500,000 people visit the city to join in the fun.

Rainbow Reveal
Kylie's outfit showcases all the joy and fun of the carnival! Her skirt twirls in a rainbow of colour and the ribbons in her hair dance in the breeze.

114

Paige
the Pantomime Fairy

When they met Paige, Kirsty and Rachel were due to perform in Cinderella. But things were not going well. Paige's three magic shoes were missing, so the costumes didn't fit, the scenery was breaking, and nobody could remember their lines!

Rainbow Reveal

Paige's favourite ever pantomime is *Sleeping Beauty*.

Flora
the Fancy Dress Fairy

Rainbow Reveal

Flora's magic items are a figurine, a cape and a mask. They make sure that all parties go without a hitch.

In this magical story, Kirsty and Rachel were staying in a real castle! Kirsty's cousin, Lindsay, was throwing a wonderful fancy dress ball. The girls couldn't wait to get dressed up! But when they stumbled across Jack Frost at the castle, they knew Lindsay's ball was in trouble. They needed Flora's help – and she needed theirs to protect her three magical items from the naughty goblins!

Chrissie
the Wish Fairy

Chrissie's wish magic allows a person holding one of her magical objects to have their wish come true. But when Rachel and Kirsty met Chrissie, her magic Christmas card, carol sheet and wooden spoon had all been stolen!

Rainbow Reveal
Chrissie adores wrapping presents with Jasmine the Present Fairy. They always make gifts look extra special.

Gabriella
the Snow Kingdom Fairy

Rainbow Reveal
Gabriella and Crystal the Snow Fairy are the best of friends!

Rachel and Kirsty were having a wonderful snowy holiday in the mountains when they met Gabriella! They were really looking forward to skiing, snowboarding and going to the Winter Festival. But no such luck – everything seemed to be going wrong! Gabriella needed Rachel and Kirsty's help to find her magic snowflake, chest full of festive spirit, and firestone, so she could put things right…

Shannon
the Ocean Fairy

Shannon loses her enchanted pearls, And tries to find them with help from the girls!

The girls were visiting Kirsty's gran in the seaside town of Leamouth when they were magically invited to a Fairyland beach party! Here they met flame-haired Shannon – who told them that Jack Frost had stolen her three enchanted pearls!

Rainbow Reveal
Lucky Shannon is friends with all of the ocean creatures and the Ocean Fairies!

Rainbow Reveal
Shannon magics two bubbles to go over Rachel and Kirsty's heads to let them breathe and speak underwater!

Mia
the Bridesmaid Fairy

Brides should carry something old, something new, Something borrowed and something blue!

Rachel and Kirsty were counting down the days until they were bridesmaids for Kirsty's cousin Esther! Preparations were going very well but a visit from Mia the Bridesmaid Fairy changed everything – something was wrong with her three magical wedding charms. The girls had to help Mia so that Esther's wedding wasn't a total disaster…

Rainbow Reveal
Mia's wedding charms are a silver sixpence, golden bells and a moonshine veil!

Rainbow Reveal
Mia is great friends with Kate the Royal Wedding Fairy.

Destiny
the Pop Star Fairy

Destiny's three magical objects are the sparkle sash, which perfects pop stars' outfits; the keepsake key, which looks after all songs and music; and the magical microphone, which makes sound and lighting work brilliantly! But mean Jack Frost once stole these magical items from the pop princess as he wanted to be the best pop star in town…

Rainbow Reveal
Rachel and Kirsty's favourite girl group is The Angels!

Belle
the Birthday Fairy

In Belle's story, Rachel and her dad had planned a surprise birthday party for Rachel's mum. But nothing seemed to be going right for anyone's special day and the two girls knew something was wrong in Fairyland…they needed to help Belle make birthdays brilliant once more!

Rainbow Reveal
Belle and the Party Fairies are always working together to make every fairy's special day magical in every way.

119

Juliet
the Valentine Fairy

A gorgeous red rose
is often a sign
Of a lovely, romantic
Valentine!

Who on earth doesn't like Valentine's Day? Jack Frost, that's who! He tried to ruin it one year by stealing Juliet's magical objects. With these objects in the hands of the silly goblins – plus a wand to cause extra trouble – the magic of Valentine's Day looked sure to be destroyed.

Rainbow Reveal
Juliet's magical objects are a Valentine's card, a red rose and a box of chocolate hearts.

Rainbow Reveal
It's traditional to send cards to people you love on Valentine's Day!

Trixie
the Halloween Fairy

Rachel and Kirsty couldn't wait to go trick-or-treating in Tippington! Every year, the children dress up and have a really fun time. But a visit from Trixie the Halloween Fairy put the girls on high alert – the greedy goblins had stolen her three Halloween sweets and with them missing, nobody could have any spooky fun.

Rainbow Reveal
With Trixie, the girls meet a little black kitten called Moonlight.

Cheryl
the Christmas Tree Fairy

Decorating a Christmas tree is such an important part of Christmas! In this story Rachel and Kirsty discovered that Cheryl's Fairyland Christmas tree was missing. This special tree looks after lots of different areas of the festive season and with it missing, the Christmas time celebrations couldn't begin…

Rainbow Reveal
Cheryl also has a magical Christmas star and Christmas gift.

Emma
the Easter Fairy

Emma makes
Easter lots of fun,
With chocolate eggs
for everyone!

A visit from Emma one year soon threatened Rachel and Kirsty's happy holiday – the Easter bunny had gone missing and Emma's three magic eggs had been stolen! The girls had to help out, before Easter was ruined.

Kate
the Royal Wedding Fairy

Kate has such a special job – she makes sure that all weddings are bursting with love and joy! When there was a royal wedding in Fairyland, mean Jack Frost stole Kate's True Love Crown. Rachel and Kirsty had to help her find it quickly, so the royal couple could live happily ever after!

Rainbow Reveal
Kate the Royal Wedding Fairy is best friends with Mia the Bridesmaid Fairy!

Florence
the Friendship Fairy

Everyone knows just how important friendship is, so Florence really is a very special fairy! Her three magic objects look after all aspects of friendship – her memory book keeps happy memories safe, her friendship ribbon lets friends have lots of fun, and her sparkly bracelet protects all friendships. But when Florence once lost her objects, Kirsty and Rachel had to use their special friendship to save the day.

Memory Book

Rainbow Reveal
Every year, Florence organises a special Friendship Day, to celebrate friendships everywhere!

Rainbow Reveal
In this story Florence and the other fairies make Rachel and Kirsty a very special friendship bracelet each, to say thank you for being such brilliant pals!

Selena
the Sleepover Fairy

Selena's job is to make all sleepovers great fun! When Rachel and Kirsty went to a big sleepover at a museum, strange things started to happen. The girls suspected it had something to do with a naughty group of children with green skin and very big noses… They helped Selena as best they could!

Rainbow Reveal
Selena often spends time with Sabrina the Sweet Dreams Fairy, swapping tips.

Rainbow Reveal
Selena's tip for sleepovers is to make a door hanger, so your family know when you and your friends are busy!

Rainbow Reveal
Selena's three magic objects are a sleeping bag, a games bag and a snack box.

Hannah
the Happy Ever After Fairy

In this special story the endings of favourite fairy tales were changed, so there were no happy-ever-afters! Hannah needed Kirsty and Rachel to help her find out what was going wrong. She knew it had something to do with mean Jack Frost and her missing quill pen…

Rainbow Reveal
Whenever Hannah uses her magic pen, rainbow-coloured sparkles fizz from the end of it.

Natalie
the Christmas Stocking Fairy

Natalie's special fairy magic makes sure opening presents from Christmas stockings is a time full of joy and happiness. But without her magical stocking, mince pie and candy cane, Natalie couldn't make Christmas morning magical…or any other part of Christmas Day!

Rainbow Reveal
Natalie's wand spills glittery silver snowflakes from the tip whenever she casts a spell.

Keira
the Film Star Fairy

When Rachel and Kirsty met Keira, they were extras in a real Hollywood movie being filmed in Tippington! Things started to go wrong on set, and the girls soon received a visit from the very glamorous little fairy who had lost her silver script, magical megaphone and enchanted clapperboard.

Keira's magic looks after each movie star, With her help and training, they all will go far!

Elizabeth
the Jubilee Fairy

Elizabeth is a fairy who glitters, shines and glows, She sparkles like a diamond from her head to her toes!

Elizabeth is a very important fairy – she makes sure that all jubilee celebrations are perfect. Rachel and Kirsty met Elizabeth in the Tower of London, and had to travel to Fairyland, and the chilly goblin village, to help her out!

Olympia
the Games Fairy

Olympia is the sportiest fairy in Fairyland! She uses her magic to make sure that sporting games and tournaments in the human world and Fairyland are fun, organised and – above all – fair!

This special fairy has the perfect sporting name, She'll always do her best to help you win your game!

Rainbow Reveal
Olympia's magic objects are a sparkling swimming cap, a musical bicycle bell and a pair of tireless trainers.

Rainbow Reveal
Olympia's magic watches over the Melford Triathlon, the Fairyland Games and the Fairyland Olympics!

Tamara
the Tooth Fairy

When Jack Frost had terrible toothache, he stole Tamara's magical moonstone ring, endless coin and enchanted pouch to try and make himself feel better. But without her objects, Tamara couldn't do her job properly and children all over the human world suffered!

Rainbow Reveal
Zara the Starlight Fairy lights Tamara's way to lost teeth.

Rainbow Reveal
Tamara loves chatting to night-time creatures!

Did you know?
Humans and fairies have four different types of teeth to help them enjoy lots of yummy food.

Angelica
the Angel Fairy

Angelica is good and kind, and uses her magic to keep Christmas time peaceful. That is, unless Jack Frost steals her magical pan pipes, snow-white feather and enchanted name scroll! When Rachel and Kirsty met Angelica, that was just what had happened!

Rainbow Reveal
The Christmas Fairies always spend Christmas Eve together!

Rainbow Reveal
Jennifer is good friends with Sabrina the Sweet Dreams Fairy.

Jennifer
the Babysitting Fairy

Jennifer works in the Fairyland Nursery and her special magic makes sure that all babies and children are well looked after! But when her toy box, snack pack and nightlight were stolen, it wasn't long before children everywhere were having a miserable time!

Nicki
the Holiday Camp Fairy

Rainbow Reveal
The girls have lockets full of fairy dust, which they use to contact their fairy friends.

Rachel and Kirsty can't wait to be spend their summer holiday together at Camp Oakwood. There are so many fun things to do! But when lots of the activities start to go horribly wrong, the girls know Nicki needs their help.

Carly
the Schoolfriend Fairy

It's time for an interschool competition, and both Rachel and Kirsty are taking part! But when a new school team appears – with cheeky green pupils – will the spelling bee, science contest and disco be fun and fair…?

Rainbow Reveal
Carly makes her uniform look super stylish with shiny brogues, knee socks and a bright pinafore dress.

Rainbow Reveal

It's not often you see Jack Frost's soft side, but he became very fond of the royal baby.

Alexandra
the Royal Baby Fairy

Did you know?

Even when fairies are very tiny, they can fly perfectly! The royal baby showed off its flying skills in this adventure.

In this adventure Kirsty and Rachel were visiting Norwood Palace, an amazing place where lots of royal princes and princesses had lived! They were so pleased when Alexandra the Royal Baby Fairy appeared but she had some terrible news for them: the new royal baby had gone missing!

Rainbow Reveal

Foster the stork has a very important job. He delivers all new royal babies to their parents! But naughty Jack Frost tricked poor Foster into giving up his precious bundle.

Robyn
the Christmas Party Fairy

Everyone loves Christmas and Rachel and Kirsty couldn't wait to organise a huge Christmas party! But with Robyn's magical objects mysteriously missing, the festive season looked like it would be a real letdown…

Rainbow Reveal
The girls got a bit of a shock when Robyn first appeared out of a Christmas cracker!

Georgie
the Royal Prince Fairy

Kirsty and Rachel were so excited to be meeting real princes in this adventure! And when Georgie magically appeared and invited them to a Fairyland naming ceremony for the new royal baby, the girls knew they were going to have the best weekend ever!

Rainbow Reveal
Georgie wears a very special golden ring with a pattern engraved on it. She uses the pattern to stamp important royal documents.

Lila & Myla
the Twins Fairies

K irsty and Rachel were at their twin friends' birthday party when everything started to go wrong! Then the girls spotted a big footprint in the ground and they knew there were goblins around…could the girls help Lila and Myla work out what the goblins were up to and stop them before they caused terrible twin trouble?

Did you know?

Twins sometimes invent their own special language that only they understand! This is called "idioglossia".

Rainbow Reveal

Lila and Myla are identical twins but there is one way to tell them apart. Myla has pink highlights in her dark hair and Lila's are blue.

Tilly
the Teacher Fairy

Tilly the Teacher Fairy has a very important job. She makes sure that everything runs smoothly at schools so that everyone has fun and learns lots! But when one of her fairy pupils accidentally makes her three magical objects disappear, sneaky Jack Frost is the first to find them. He is determined to use these to cause trouble and mischief!

Rainbow Reveal
Jack Frost has set up a special goblin school next to the Ice Palace. But even with the help of Tilly's magical objects, it's hard to teach the naughty goblins anything!

Rainbow Reveal
In this adventure a new ICT centre is opening at Rachel's school. But all the computers are broken and all that's showing on the screens is a giant snowflake...

Rainbow Reveal
One of Tilly's magical objects is a magic apple. Greedy Jack Frost told his pupils that whoever gave him the best present would win the apple!

King Oberon and Queen Titania

King Oberon and Queen Titania are the wise and kind rulers of Fairyland! They look after all the fairies and magical creatures that live in their kingdom.

Rainbow Reveal

The royal couple know that the Rainbow Magic Fairies love to sing, dance and have fun! They make sure lots of wonderful parties are held throughout the year, with many taking place at the Fairyland Palace.

Rainbow Reveal

King Oberon and Queen Titania were so excited when their niece, Princess Grace, had a baby! The royal rulers often babysit their great-nephew, and he loves to flutter around the palace.

Rainbow Reveal

The royal rulers are used to magnificent Fairyland feasts. But one of their favourite treats is a simple picnic in the grounds of the palace. Lovely Coco the Cupcake Fairy sometimes bakes delicious cupcakes for these occasions!

Kirsty and Rachel

Kirsty's Reveal

Kirsty is loyal, fun-loving and adventurous! She lives on a street called Wether Way in Wetherbury Village with her mum and dad.

Ever since Rachel and Kirsty met, they've been the very best of friends! Although they don't live near to each other, they get together whenever they can and they always have wonderful, magical adventures.

Kirsty's Reveal

Kirsty has a pet cat called Pearl. Pearl is very cute and has a tiny white smudge on her head!

Kirsty's Reveal

Kirsty loves the beautiful locket given to her and Rachel by Queen Titania. The locket is full of magical fairy dust.

Kirsty's Reveal

Kirsty just loves to fly! She's always so excited when the fairies use their wands to give the girls gossamer wings.

Rachel's Reveal

Rachel is friendly, caring and creative! She lives in Tippington Town with her mum and dad and an Old English Sheepdog called Buttons.

Rachel's Reveal

Kind Rachel sometimes feels sorry for Jack Frost! Although he is very naughty, she has spotted that he has a soft side.

Rachel's Reveal

Rachel loves all of her adventures with the Rainbow Magic fairies, and the one with Mia the Bridesmaid Fairy was extra special. Not only did Kirsty and Rachel help Mia make sure weddings everywhere went well, but they were also bridesmaids for Kirsty's cousin!

Rachel's Reveal

Rachel loves the amazing musical box given to them when she and Kirsty helped the Music Fairies. The soft music reminds Rachel of magical times with her fairy friends!

Rachel's Reveal

Rachel's favourite colours are purple and lilac.

Jack Frost and the Goblins

Jack Frost and his goblins love to cause trouble for the Rainbow Magic Fairies. Even though the fairies are always kind to the naughty creatures, the Ice Lord loves to think up new ways for his green gang to make mischief!

Goblin Reveal
Goblins are very greedy. They are too lazy to cook so they often sneak around Fairyland and the human world pinching food and leaving big goblin footprints behind!

Frost Reveal
Vain Jack Frost thinks he is the best musician ever! When his goblins stole the Music Fairies' instruments, their powerful magic made Jack Frost and his Gobolicious Band sound brilliant.

Goblin Reveal
Goblins have always worked for Jack Frost. Some goblins live in the chilly Ice Castle and others have houses in the little village nearby.

Goblin Reveal
Goblins hate having cold feet more than anything in the world. It makes them very grumpy.

Frost Reveal
One of the reasons Jack Frost spends so much time causing trouble for the fairies is because he's a bit bored. He gets his goblins to do all his chores for him!

Rainspell Island

Rainspell Island is the most magical place in the human world! It was here that Rachel and Kirsty met and had their very first adventure with the fairies.

Rainbow Reveal
Rachel's favourite place on the island is Mrs Merry's cottage. Kirsty loves visiting the rockpools on the beach!

Rainbow Reveal
The first thing that Rachel and Kirsty saw when they got close to Rainspell was a beautiful rainbow. Little did they know that Ruby was at the end of it!

Rainbow Reveal
Rainspell Island is not the only magical location in the world. There are lots of special places scattered around.

Rainbow Reveal
Rachel and Kirsty have returned to Rainspell Island lots of times! They have enjoyed adventures with the Green Fairies and the Magical Crafts Fairies on the island.

Dear Fairy Friend,

We hope you've enjoyed reading our book and finding out lots about the Rainbow Magic Fairies. We've loved spending this special time with you!

Remember to have fun, look after your family and friends and always believe in magic. Keep your eyes open for fairies, as you never know when we might flutter by!

With much love and sparkly fairy magic,

The Rainbow Magic Fairies
xxxxxxx

Have you read them all?

The Rainbow Fairies
1. Ruby the Red Fairy ☐
2. Amber the Orange Fairy ☐
3. Saffron the Yellow Fairy ☐
4. Fern the Green Fairy ☐
5. Sky the Blue Fairy ☐
6. Izzy the Indigo Fairy ☐
7. Heather the Violet Fairy ☐

The Weather Fairies
8. Crystal the Snow Fairy ☐
9. Abigail the Breeze Fairy ☐
10. Pearl the Cloud Fairy ☐
11. Goldie the Sunshine Fairy ☐
12. Evie the Mist Fairy ☐
13. Storm the Lightning Fairy ☐
14. Hayley the Rain Fairy ☐

The Party Fairies
15. Cherry the Cake Fairy ☐
16. Melodie the Music Fairy ☐
17. Grace the Glitter Fairy ☐
18. Honey the Sweet Fairy ☐
19. Polly the Party Fun Fairy ☐
20. Phoebe the Fashion Fairy ☐
21. Jasmine the Present Fairy ☐

The Jewel Fairies
22. India the Moonstone Fairy ☐
23. Scarlett the Garnet Fairy ☐
24. Emily the Emerald Fairy ☐
25. Chloe the Topaz Fairy ☐
26. Amy the Amethyst Fairy ☐
27. Sophie the Sapphire Fairy ☐
28. Lucy the Diamond Fairy ☐

The Pet Keeper Fairies
29. Katie the Kitten Fairy ☐
30. Bella the Bunny Fairy ☐
31. Georgia the Guinea Pig Fairy ☐
32. Lauren the Puppy Fairy ☐
33. Harriet the Hamster Fairy ☐
34. Molly the Goldfish Fairy ☐
35. Penny the Pony Fairy ☐

The Fun Day Fairies
36. Megan the Monday Fairy ☐
37. Tallulah the Tuesday Fairy ☐
38. Willow the Wednesday Fairy ☐
39. Thea the Thursday Fairy ☐
40. Freya the Friday Fairy ☐
41. Sienna the Saturday Fairy ☐
42. Sarah the Sunday Fairy ☐

The Petal Fairies
43. Tia the Tulip Fairy ☐
44. Pippa the Poppy Fairy ☐
45. Louise the Lily Fairy ☐
46. Charlotte the Sunflower Fairy ☐
47. Olivia the Orchid Fairy ☐
48. Danielle the Daisy Fairy ☐
49. Ella the Rose Fairy ☐

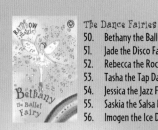

The Dance Fairies
50. Bethany the Ballet Fairy ☐
51. Jade the Disco Fairy ☐
52. Rebecca the Rock'n'Roll Fairy ☐
53. Tasha the Tap Dance Fairy ☐
54. Jessica the Jazz Fairy ☐
55. Saskia the Salsa Fairy ☐
56. Imogen the Ice Dance Fairy ☐

The Sporty Fairies
57. Helena the Horseriding Fairy ☐
58. Francesca the Football Fairy ☐
59. Zoe the Skating Fairy ☐
60. Naomi the Netball Fairy ☐
61. Samantha the Swimming Fairy ☐
62. Alice the Tennis Fairy ☐
63. Gemma the Gymnastics Fairy ☐

The Music Fairies
64. Poppy the Piano Fairy ☐
65. Ellie the Guitar Fairy ☐
66. Fiona the Flute Fairy ☐
67. Danni the Drum Fairy ☐
68. Maya the Harp Fairy ☐
69. Victoria the Violin Fairy ☐
70. Sadie the Saxophone Fairy ☐

The Magical Animal Fairies
71. Ashley the Dragon Fairy ☐
72. Lara the Black Cat Fairy ☐
73. Erin the Firebird Fairy ☐
74. Rihanna the Seahorse Fairy ☐
75. Sophia the Snow Swan Fairy ☐
76. Leona the Unicorn Fairy ☐
77. Caitlin the Ice Bear Fairy ☐

The Green Fairies
78. Nicole the Beach Fairy ☐
79. Isabella the Air Fairy ☐
80. Edie the Garden Fairy ☐
81. Coral the Reef Fairy ☐
82. Lily the Rainforest Fairy ☐
83. Carrie the Snow Cap Fairy ☐
84. Milly the River Fairy ☐

The Ocean Fairies
85. Ally the Dolphin Fairy ☐
86. Amelie the Seal Fairy ☐
87. Pia the Penguin Fairy ☐
88. Tess the Sea Turtle Fairy ☐
89. Stephanie the Starfish Fairy ☐
90. Whitney the Whale Fairy ☐
91. Courtney the Clownfish Fairy ☐

The Twilight Fairies
92. Ava the Sunset Fairy ☐
93. Lexi the Firefly Fairy ☐
94. Zara the Starlight Fairy ☐
95. Morgan the Midnight Fairy ☐
96. Yasmin the Night Owl Fairy ☐
97. Maisie the Moonbeam Fairy ☐
98. Sabrina the Sweet Dreams Fairy ☐

The Showtime Fairies
99. Madison the Magic Show Fairy ☐
100. Leah the Theatre Fairy ☐
101. Alesha the Acrobat Fairy ☐
102. Darcey the Dance Diva Fairy ☐
103. Taylor the Talent Show Fairy ☐
104. Amelia the Singing Fairy ☐
105. Isla the Ice Star Fairy ☐

The Princess Fairies
106. Honor the Happy Days Fairy ☐
107. Demi the Dressing-Up Fairy ☐
108. Anya the Cuddly Creatures Fairy ☐
109. Elisa the Adventure Fairy ☐
110. Lizzie the Sweet Treats Fairy ☐
111. Maddie the Playtime Fairy ☐
112. Eva the Enchanted Ball Fairy ☐

The Pop Star Fairies
113. Jessie the Lyrics Fairy ☐
114. Adele the Singing Coach Fairy ☐
115. Vanessa the Dance Steps Fairy ☐
116. Miley the Stylist Fairy ☐
117. Frankie the Make-Up Fairy ☐
118. Rochelle the Star Spotter Fairy ☐
119. Una the Concert Fairy ☐

The Fashion Fairies
120. Miranda the Beauty Fairy ☐
121. Claudia the Accessories Fairy ☐
12.2. Tyra the Dress Designer Fairy ☐
123. Alexa the Fashion Reporter Fairy ☐
124. Matilda the Hair Stylist Fairy ☐
125. Brooke the Photographer Fairy ☐
126. Lola the Fashion Fairy ☐

The Sweet Fairies
127. Lottie the Lollipop Fairy ☐
128. Esme the Ice Cream Fairy ☐
129. Coco the Cupcake Fairy ☐
130. Clara the Chocolate Fairy ☐
131. Madeleine the Cookie Fairy ☐
132. Layla the Candyfloss Fairy ☐
133. Nina the Birthday Cake Fairy ☐

The Baby Animal Rescue Fairies
134. Mae the Panda Fairy ☐
135. Kitty the Tiger Fairy ☐
136. Mara the Meerkat Fairy ☐
137. Savannah the Zebra Fairy ☐
138. Kimberley the Koala Fairy ☐
139. Rosie the Honey Bear Fairy ☐
140. Anna the Arctic Fox Fairy ☐

The Magical Crafts Fairies
141. Kayla the Pottery Fairy ☐
142. Annabelle the Drawing Fairy ☐
143. Zadie the Sewing Fairy ☐
144. Josie the Jewellery-Making Fairy ☐
145. Violet the Painting Fairy ☐
146. Libby the Story-Writing Fairy ☐
147. Roxie the Baking Fairy ☐

Holiday specials – three books in one!

 ☐ Holly the Christmas Fairy

☐ Summer the Holiday Fairy

 ☐ Stella the Star Fairy

 ☐ Kylie the Carnival Fairy

 ☐ Paige the Pantomime Fairy

 ☐ Flora the Fancy Dress Fairy

 ☐ Chrissie the Wish Fairy

☐ Shannon the Ocean Fairy

 ☐ Gabriella the Snow Kingdom Fairy

☐ Mia the Bridesmaid Fairy

☐ Destiny the Pop Star Fairy

☐ Juliet the Valentine Fairy

☐ Belle the Birthday Fairy

 ☐ Trixie the Halloween Fairy

 ☐ Cheryl the Christmas Tree Fairy

☐ Florence the Friendship Fairy

☐ Emma the Easter Fairy

☐ Kate the Royal Wedding Fairy

☐ Selena the Sleepover Fairy

☐ Natalie the Christmas Stocking Fairy

 ☐ Keira the Film Star Fairy

 ☐ Olympia the Games Fairy

 ☐ Tamara the Tooth Fairy

☐ Elizabeth the Jubilee Fairy

☐ Angelica the Angel Fairy

☐ Jennifer the Babysitter Fairy

 ☐ Nicki the Holiday Camp Fairy

☐ Alexandra the Royal Baby Fairy

 ☐ Carly the Schoolfriend Fairy

 ☐ Robyn the Christmas Party Fairy

   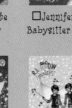       ☐ Georgie the Royal Prince Fairy

☐ Lila & Myla the Twins Fairies

☐ Tilly the Teacher Fairy

There's a book of fairy fun for everyone!

www.rainbowmagicbooks.co.uk

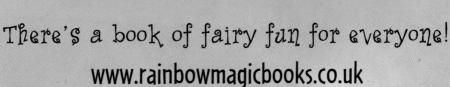

RAINBOW
magic

Become a
Rainbow Magic
fairy friend and be the first to
see sneak peeks of new books.

There are lots of special offers and exclusive
competitions to win sparkly
Rainbow Magic prizes.

Sign up today at
www.rainbowmagicbooks.co.uk